JAZZ TRUMPET
SCALES
INTRODUCTION

All good jazz sounds effortless, but that sense of ease is usually achieved through regular hard work on technique, including the practice of scales and arpeggios. Through devoting a few minutes of each practice session to this area you can improve many aspects of your playing, such as pulse and rhythm, finger dexterity, embouchure strength, tone production and familiarity with the sounds of chords. The main function of the scales presented here, however, is to encourage flexibility through technical control and familiarity with the geography of your instrument. They also introduce you to the melodic and rhythmic vocabulary of jazz, including its feels, patterns, roots and key centres.

The scales syllabus includes the simplest and most common roots and keys of jazz (e.g. concert C, F, B♭ and E♭), and covers modes, pentatonic scales and chord shapes as they appear in tunes set for the Level/Grade. It is designed specifically to enable you to work in a range of ways in these more common keys, rather than covering all twelve keys to the same depth.

Because the scales integrate with the set tunes, you can immediately use patterns from the scales syllabus in your improvising. Inclusion of a phrase in a particular key in the tune books does not necessarily imply that the scale of that key *on the tonic* has been covered, although there will always be a scale that accommodates the phrase. For example, you could have a tune in C but not have a C major scale; you will, however, have at least one related scale, such as G mixolydian, to give you the shapes you need.

Working systematically through the scheme of the book will inform the musical choices you make while improvising. Imaginative playing, however, will not result from unimaginative scale practice! Be flexible and mix your technical work with improvisation, turning each exercise into a piece of music as soon as you can. Think of ways of practising which are directly relevant to your needs as a player and to the tune you wish to play.

© 2003 by The Associated Board of the Royal Schools of Music
Printed in England by Halstan & Co. Ltd, Amersham, Bucks.,
on materials from sustainable sources
Reprinted in 2018

JAZZ TRUMPET
SCALES
INTRODUCTION

PLAYING SCALES IN THE EXAM

Swing or straight 8s

The examiner will ask for a scale to be played in one of three ways: 'swing', 'straight-8s tongued' or 'straight-8s slurred'. It is important that scales are practised in each of these ways.

Swing

Jazz musicians approach swing in an enormous variety of ways, and at a professional level swing is personal to every player; Miles Davis, for example, will tongue scalic runs differently from Clifford Brown. Many factors are involved, including the interaction between musicians, the era of jazz in question, and the speed of each tune. Playing scales in swing 8s will help you develop the skills of swing, by focusing you on the pulse, on subdivision, on tonguing appropriately and on stressed and unstressed notes.

Unfortunately swing cannot be notated with precision. Sometimes swing 8s are written as ♪♪ for example, whereas ABRSM's preferred notation is the more common ♫

Swing can take many forms, and in the end the only way to learn to play swing is to listen to recordings of the best players, and to attend live gigs. In the meantime, here are some starting points:

- always make the quarter-note (crotchet) pulse clear
- begin by thinking of swing as in a smooth, relaxed triplet feel, which varies according to the speed and style of the music played
- stress (add weight to) the offbeat, or reduce weight on ('ghost') the onbeat. This can be visualized as:
  ▬ ▬ ▬ ▬ ▬ etc.

In swing, use one of the following two articulations.

1. Tonguing every note, add a little weight to the offbeat:

Tongue clearly and, as experience allows, try to tongue notes without 'bumping' them, so that the flow is maintained.

2. Tonguing the offbeat, apply weight to the offbeat and slur to the onbeat:

JAZZ TRUMPET
SCALES
INTRODUCTION

Both of the above may also be played starting on the offbeat. Thus, in example 1 – tonguing every note – start between beats and apply weight to the offbeat:

In example 2 – tonguing the offbeat – apply weight to the offbeat and slur to the onbeat:

Candidates may start swing scales and arpeggios either on or off the beat.

Straight 8s

In the exam, straight-8s scales are tongued or slurred, as directed by the examiner. All straight-8s scales must start **on** the beat.

Tongued
- play even straight 8s (quavers)
- tongue each note but keep the line flowing
- put equal weight on the onbeat and offbeat and use even tone throughout

Slurred
- play even straight 8s (quavers)
- tongue the first note and then run each note smoothly into the next, without tonguing
- put equal weight on the onbeat and offbeat and use even tone throughout

General guidelines

All scales and arpeggios must be played from memory. The examiner will normally ask for at least one pattern from each type of scale or arpeggio required at that Level/Grade, and will aim to hear a balance of both straight 8s and swing. All keys will be stated at the pitch of the candidate's instrument.

Where possible, breathing should be incorporated so as to maintain the melodic line. Examiners understand that taking a breath in the course of a longer pattern is sometimes unavoidable with younger candidates, particularly at Levels/Grades 1–3.

JAZZ TRUMPET
SCALES
INTRODUCTION

The table below gives the recommended **minimum** speeds.

Level/Grade	scales	arpeggios
1	♩ = 50	♪ = 72
2	♩ = 56	♪ = 80
3	♩ = 66	♪ = 92
4	♩ = 72	♪ = 100
5	♩ = 80	♪ = 112

Finally, the following checklist explains what the examiner will be looking for in your playing:

- an even and positive sense of pulse and rhythm, at or above the minimum tempo
- accurate and fluent realization from memory of the scale patterns set for the Level/Grade
- confident, controlled and flexible tone, with good intonation across the pitch range of the Level/Grade
- independence of the fingers
- even tonguing and clearly defined articulation
- smooth negotiation of common technical problems

LEVEL/GRADE 1

Scales
Straight 8s or swing

DORIAN on A
1 octave

MIXOLYDIAN on C
1 octave

F MAJOR
to a fifth

MAJOR PENTATONIC on C
1 octave

MINOR PENTATONIC on A
1 octave

Arpeggio
Straight 8s or swing

C MAJOR
1 octave

LEVEL/GRADE 2

Scales
Straight 8s or swing

DORIAN on D
1 octave

MIXOLYDIAN on B♭
1 octave

G MAJOR
to a fifth

B♭ MAJOR
1 octave

MAJOR PENTATONIC on D
1 octave

Arpeggios
Straight 8s or swing

B♭ MAJOR
1 octave

A MINOR
1 octave

LEVEL/GRADE 3

Scales

Straight 8s or swing

DORIAN on E
1 octave

MIXOLYDIAN on E
1 octave

LYDIAN on B♭
1 octave

D MAJOR
1 octave

E♭ MAJOR
1 octave

MAJOR PENTATONIC on A
1 octave

MINOR PENTATONIC on E
1 octave

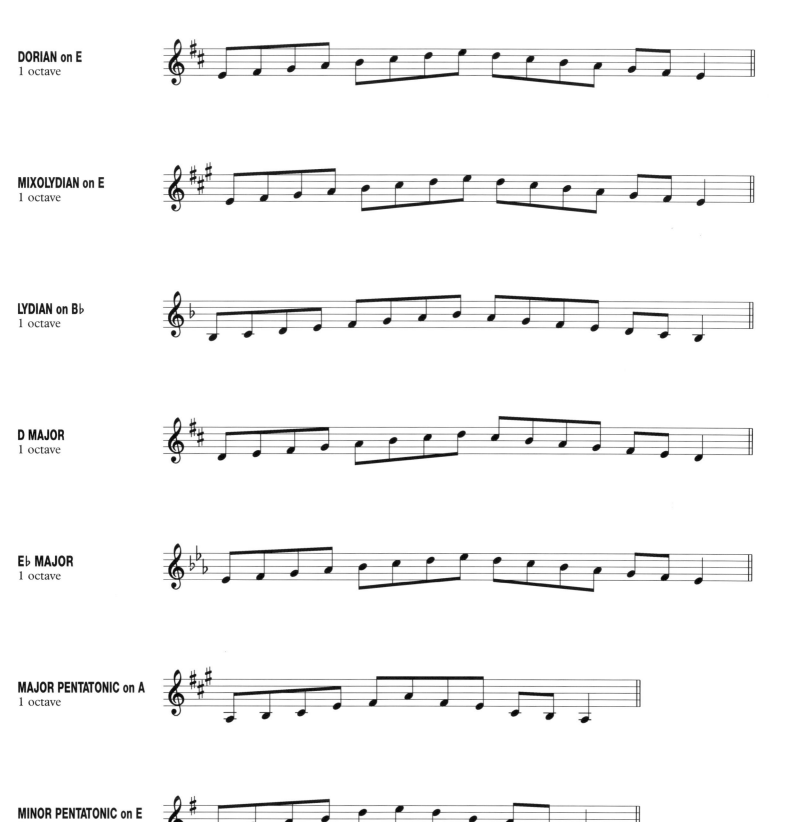

LEVEL/GRADE 3

BLUES SCALE on C
1 octave

CHROMATIC on C
1 octave

Arpeggios
Straight 8s or swing

E♭ MAJOR
1 octave

C MINOR
1 octave

LEVEL/GRADE 4

Scales
Straight 8s or swing

DORIAN on A
to a twelfth

MIXOLYDIAN on F
1 octave

LYDIAN on F
1 octave

LYDIAN on A♭
to a twelfth

E MAJOR
1 octave

MAJOR PENTATONIC on F
1 octave

MINOR PENTATONIC on C
1 octave

BLUES SCALE on F
1 octave

LEVEL/GRADE 4

CHROMATIC on B♭
to a twelfth

Arpeggios

Straight 8s or swing

A MAJOR
to a twelfth

B MINOR
to a twelfth

E♭△9
to a ninth

E♭9
to a ninth

E♭m9
to a ninth

LEVEL/GRADE 5

Scales

Straight 8s or swing

DORIAN on B
to a twelfth

MIXOLYDIAN on A
to a twelfth

LYDIAN on C
to a twelfth

C MAJOR
to a twelfth

D♭ MAJOR
to a twelfth

MAJOR PENTATONIC on A♭
2 octaves

MINOR PENTATONIC on G
2 octaves

BLUES SCALE on B♭
1 octave

CHROMATIC on C
to a twelfth

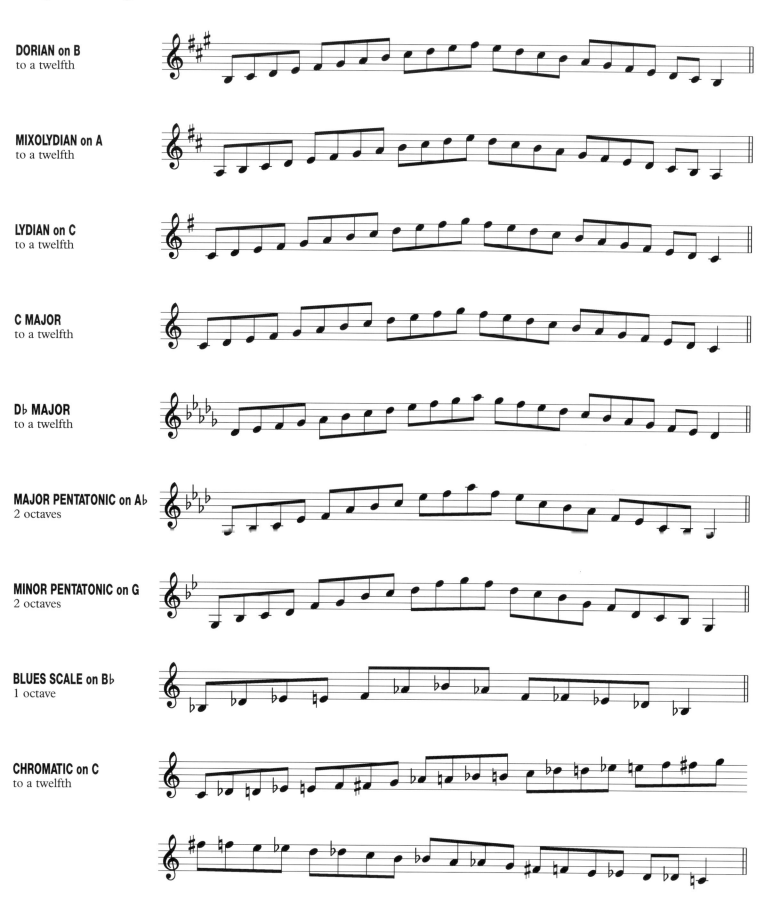

Arpeggios

Straight 8s or swing

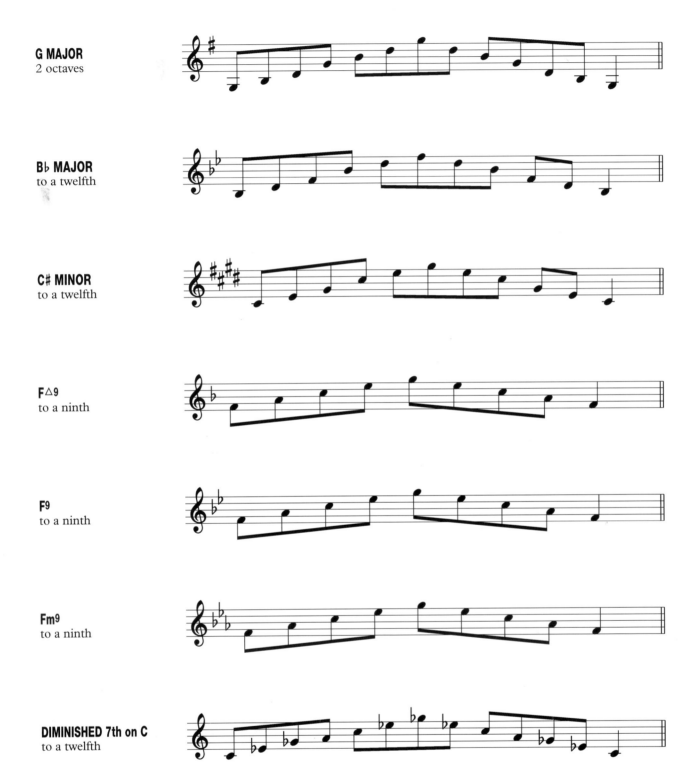

G MAJOR
2 octaves

B♭ MAJOR
to a twelfth

C♯ MINOR
to a twelfth

F△9
to a ninth

F9
to a ninth

Fm9
to a ninth

DIMINISHED 7th on C
to a twelfth